big
NATE
I CAN'T TAKE IT!

More

adventures from

LINCOLN PEIRCE

big NATE

I CAN'T TAKE IT!

by LINCOLN PEIRCE

Andrews McMeel
Publishing, LLC
Kansas City • Sydney • London

Big Nate is distributed internationally by Universal Uclick.

Big Nate: I Can't Take It! copyright © 2013 by United Feature Syndicate.
All rights reserved. Printed in China. No part of this book may be used or
reproduced in any manner whatsoever without written permission except in the
case of reprints in the context of reviews.

Andrews McMeel Publishing, LLC
an Andrews McMeel Universal company
1130 Walnut Street, Kansas City, Missouri 64106

www.andrewsmcmeel.com

13 14 15 16 17 SDB 10 9 8 7 6 5 4 3 2 1

ISBN: 978-1-4494-2937-9

Library of Congress Control Number: 2013933500

Made by:
Shenzhen Donnelley Printing Company Ltd.
Address and location of manufacturer:
No. 47, Wuhe Nan Road, Bantian Ind. Zone,
Shenzhen China, 518129
1st Printing – 7/29/13

Big Nate can be viewed on the Internet at
www.gocomics.com/big_nate

A SHLOX-TV REALITY special:
NEW YEAR'S EVE
with
ELLEN WRIGHT!

OUR — HEROINE

with your hosts:
BIFF BIFFWELL — CHIP CHIPSON

It's December 31st, Chip, and a typical teen ELLEN WRIGHT is preparing for...

...a ROCKIN' NEW YEAR'S PARTY!

DING DONG!

...And here's her date! Loyal yet hapless boyfriend GORDIE!

The poor sap.

We will now FOLLOW Ellen and Gordie to the party and provide a LIVE report from...

HOLD ON, Biff! Not so fast!

There'll be a slight delay! Ellen needs to...

← Dramatic pause

"FRESHEN UP"!

dismayed expression →

Why don't you handle the play-by-play, Chip?

Right, Biff! She's reaching for the foundation...

Now the blush... the concealer... the rouge... the eyeshadow... the mascara...

EGAD! Will it NEVER END??

Hey, when you look like Ellen, you've got to go ALL OUT!

Good point, Biff.

ALMOST READY!

2001...

...A FACE ODYSSEY.

YOU'LL HAVE 45 MINUTES TO COMPLETE THIS TEST.

OKAY, HERE WE GO! NUMBER ONE!...

I'LL COME BACK TO THAT ONE.

NUMBER TWO...

UMM.... I'LL COME BACK TO THAT ONE, TOO.

NUMBER THREE... HEY, WHAT **IS** THIS? I HARDLY KNOW **ANY** OF THESE!

mumble

huh?

?

?

?

grumble

WHOOPS! MY APOLOGIES, PEOPLE! I GAVE YOU THE **WRONG TEST!**

I GAVE YOU THE TEST FOR MY **OTHER** CLASS! THEY'RE TWO CHAPTERS AHEAD OF YOU!

HERE'S THE **RIGHT** TEST!

AS I SAID, YOU HAVE 45 MINUTES.

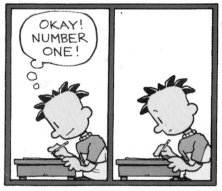

OKAY! NUMBER ONE!

CAN I HAVE THE OTHER TEST BACK?

Investigative Reporter
CHIP CHIPSON presents:

BURNING ISSUES!

Friends, today's "burning issue" is BULLYING! And here to discuss it is celebrity psychologist DR. WARREN FUZZY!

Chip, bullying is the scourge of our schools!

We all remember what it's like to be bullied! We've all felt POWERLESS!

...but what we DON'T REALIZE is how powerless the BULLIES feel!

The BULLIES feel powerless??

Right, Chip! That's why they're bullies!

They're COMPENSATING for their underlying sense of inadequacy! Underneath, they're COWARDS!

Once we know that, we can STAND UP to the bullies and STOP the cycle of bullying!

NATE.

HMM?

I'M WATCHING YOU, MISTER.

Does that really work?

Unless they're teachers. Then you just live in fear.

WHAT **HAP**PENED? MY BACK WENT OUT DURING THIRD PERIOD.

I'M IN AGONY.

I KNOW WHAT'LL HELP! GET ON THE FLOOR!

MY BROTHER-IN-LAW IS A CHIROPRACTOR! I SAW HIM DO THIS ONCE!

BY APPLYING PRESSURE TO THE RIGHT SPOT, I CAN SHIFT YOUR SPINE BACK INTO ALIGNMENT!

MMPH!

ARRGH!

EVER SEEN THE INSIDE OF THE TEACHERS' LOUNGE?

NOPE.

GIVE YOU A BUCK IF YOU PEEK INSIDE!

YOU'RE ON!

A BUCK DOESN'T COMPENSATE ME FOR THE NIGHT-MARES I'LL BE HAVING ALL SUMMER.

NATE!

YIP!

WOULD YOU MIND EXPLAINING **WHY** YOU'RE BRINGING A **ROCK** INTO SCHOOL?!

IT'S A COUNTER-WEIGHT!

A COUNTER-WEIGHT.

SO I WON'T TIP OVER!

MY BACKPACK IS SO LOADED DOWN WITH HOMEWORK I CAN'T **WALK** NORMALLY!

"PSYCH-OUT" TIME!

WELL, WELL! NUMBER 23!

NUMBER 23 ON YOUR JERSEY... ON YOUR WRISTBAND... YOUR SOCKS... YOUR SNEAKERS....

TRYING TO "BE LIKE MIKE", HUH? THAT'S SAD, MAN.

SAD?

YEAH. SORT OF PATHETIC, Y'KNOW?

YOU'RE TRYING TO BE MICHAEL JORDAN! IT'S NOT GONNA HAPPEN! YOU HAVE **NO** CHANCE!

MYSELF, I DON'T LIVE VICARIOUSLY THROUGH **OTHER** PEOPLE! I DON'T PATTERN MYSELF AFTER **ANYONE**!

SO YOU'RE TRYING TO BE... NOBODY.

EXACTLY.

YOU'RE SUCCEEDING.

I NEED TO WORK ON MY TRASH TALK.

CAN YOU GO DO IT ON THE BENCH?

LOOKING AT OLD YEARBOOKS AGAIN?

YUP! THESE PHOTOS FROM FIFTEEN YEARS AGO ARE A **RIOT**!

HEE HEE! LOOK AT PRINCIPAL NICHOLS BACK THEN!

YEAH, I... HEL-**LO**! WHO'S **THIS**?

"MS. LESSARD, SOCIAL STUDIES"! YOWZA! SHE'S **HOT**!

ROWR! SHE'S **ATOMIC**!

WHY CAN'T **WE** HAVE A TEACHER WHO LOOKS LIKE THAT?

WHAT'S UP, GENTS?

LOOK WHO WAS TEACHING SOCIAL STUDIES HERE FIFTEEN YEARS AGO!

WHAT A FOX, EH?

THAT'S MRS. GODFREY.

"LESSARD" WAS HER NAME BEFORE SHE GOT MARRIED.

I'M GOING TO BE VERY, VERY, VERY, VERY, VERY, VERY, VERY, VERY, VERY, VERY, VERY, VERY SICK.

Uh-oh! Nate and Ellen Wright are fighting again! This looks like a job for...

...DOCTOR **WARREN FUZZY,** "Feelings Specialist"!

Let's HEAL!

Kids! Accusations and anger are **NOT** the answer! Let's start a **DIALOGUE!**

Now sit down and **LOOK** at each other! **THAT'S** it!

Now, Nate... Tell Ellen: "**When** you _____, I feel _____"

But she...!

Tut TUT **TUT!** "When you _____, I feel _____."

When you act like a **Pinhead,** I **feel** like I'm going to hurl.

WONDERFUL! What have you learned about yourself?

That Ellen's a pinhead?

EXACTLY!

WHEN YOU DRAW INSULTING COMICS ABOUT ME, I FEEL LIKE WRINGING YOUR SCRAWNY LITTLE NECK.

WELL, NOW! LET'S CHECK OUT THE "TV GUIDE" AND SEE WHAT'S ON!

WE COULD WATCH THE HOCKEY GAME... OH, **NO** WE CAN'T! IT'S ON **CABLE**!

HERE'S A SHOW ABOUT THE GREAT PYRAMIDS! **OOPS**! **THAT'S** ON CABLE **TOO**!

SAY, HERE'S A GOOD MOVIE!... BUT **GUESS WHAT**?... IT'S ON **CABLE**!

GEE, I GUESS SITTING HERE READING THE TV GUIDE IS KIND OF **POINT**LESS, **ISN'T** IT, DAD?

YES

TRY READING THIS INSTEAD.

"GREAT EXPECTATIONS."

AND NO COMMERCIALS!

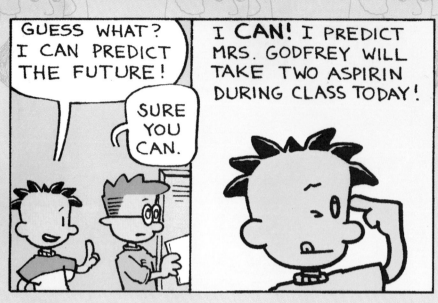

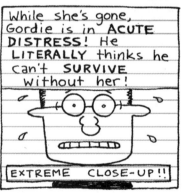

DAD, I HAVE TO DRAW A PORTRAIT OF SOMEONE FOR ART CLASS. WILL YOU SIT FOR ME?

WHY, SURE!

OKAY, WHY DON'T YOU SIT OVER HERE, AND I'LL...

NO, LET'S USE **THIS** CHAIR. IT HAS A NICER PATTERN.

NOW, LOOK STRAIGHT AHEAD AND...

ACTUALLY, WHY DON'T WE DO A THREE-QUARTERS VIEW? THAT WILL LOOK BETTER.

...AND LET'S TURN DOWN THE LIGHTS A BIT! IT'S TOO HARSH! TOO GLARING!

NATE, DON'T HOLD YOUR PAD IN YOUR LAP LIKE THAT! TILT IT UP SO YOU CAN **LOOK** AT ME WHILE YOU DRAW!

WHAT ARE YOU DOING? DON'T MOVE AROUND! THAT'LL CHANGE THE PERSPECTIVE! YOU'LL HAVE TO START OVER!

I'M DONE.

Hee Haw

FOR MY ASSIGNMENT, I WAS SUPPOSED TO DO A REPORT ON THE "LINCOLN-DOUGLAS DEBATES".

BUT I COULDN'T! **WHY?** BECAUSE THERE **IS** NOBODY NAMED "LINCOLN DOUGLAS"!

BELIEVE ME, I **LOOKED!** I FOUND **PLENTY** OF DOUGLASES, BUT WERE ANY OF THEM **LINCOLN** DOUGLASES? **NO!**

...BUT HEY! LET'S SAY THERE **WAS** SOME TOTALLY OBSCURE GUY NAMED LINCOLN DOUGLAS! WHAT WERE THESE **DEBATES** ALL ABOUT? WHAT'S UP WITH **THAT?**

WHO WAS LINCOLN DOUGLAS DEBATING? WHEN DID IT HAPPEN? IF ANYBODY KNOWS, **TELL** ME, BECAUSE **I** CERTAINLY HAVE NO CLUE!

SO ANYWAY, YOU SEE MY PREDICAMENT! HOW CAN I WRITE A REPORT ON SOME CLOWN WHO NEVER **EXISTED?**

OBVIOUSLY, I **CAN'T!** SO INSTEAD, I DREW THIS GIANT QUESTION MARK TO FOREVER SYMBOLIZE THE UNKNOWABLE MYSTERY OF... LINCOLN DOUGLAS!

CLAP! CLAP! CLAP! CLAP! CLAP! CLAP! CLAP!

THANK YOU! THANK YOU!

CRIPES.

SHLOX-TV presents...

SURVIVE...
OR ELSE!!

with your host:
KEN DOOLITTLE!!

Here we are again, friends, in the **Social Studies class-room** where our intrepid survivors have been **TRAPPED** since early September!

Z

They've had to endure countless hardships...

Have we **EVER**! Lectures, film strips, pop quizzes... Oh, the **HORROR**!

whimper

...And it's all because of **MRS. GODFREY**! She's making it **IMPOSSIBLE** to survive in here!

NATE - 6th grade tribe

Hmm... Sounds like you want to vote Mrs. Godfrey **OUT** of the classroom!

Oh, I **DO**!

So do I!

Me too!

And me!

Well, Mrs. Godfrey, the survivors have voted, and it looks like you're —

HOLD it, Ken. I didn't cast **MY** vote.

But...

No buts! What these "survivors" think is **IRRELEVANT**! I'm not going **ANYWHERE**!

I run this classroom, and **I** decide who stays and who goes!

EEEEOOWWRRRr

CHUCKLE HA HA CHUCKL
MMPH HEE HEE SNICKER HEE
HEE HE

BEEEYOWWRRr

A HA HA HA H
HA HA HA HA

NATE! WHAT IS GOING ON?

ER... MY... MY STOMACH WAS GROWLING!

WELL, YOUR STOMACH IS DISRUPTING THE CLASS! DO SOMETHING ABOUT IT!

RUSTLE
RUSTLE
CRINKLE
MUNCH
SLURP

GOT ANY SALT?

WHAT?

DETENTION

EEEYOWWWRRR...

MRS. CZERWICKI

47

Time Once Again For...

"WHAT'S YOUR OCCUPATION"?

Here's your host: BIFF BIFFWELL!

Today, friends, I'm speaking to an actual ARTISTIC MUSE!

Right, Biff! I'm the official muse of P.S. 38 Art Teacher MR. ROSA!

What does an artistic muse DO, exactly?

I help him think up assignments! Those babies don't invent themSELVES!

Who do you think came up with the "linoleum print" project? Who created the "saran-wrap stained-glass-window" assignment? ME!

Very impressive!

But TIRING! Being that creative is EXHAUSTING!

Why don't you take a vacation?

And leave Mr. Rosa to think up projects HIMSELF? I don't know....

Oh, come on! You DESERVE it!

You know, you're RIGHT! For his next class, Mr. Rosa is ON HIS OWN!

"FREE DRAWING," PEOPLE.

LAME.

★☆★☆★☆★☆★
Time For Another
Scintillating Edition OF...

FACULTY
INTERVIEW!

with your host:
CHIP CHIPSON!

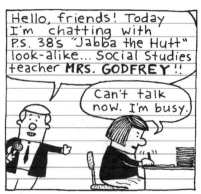

Hello, friends! Today I'm chatting with P.S. 38's "Jabba the Hutt" look-alike... Social Studies teacher **MRS. GODFREY**!!

Can't talk now. I'm busy.

Ah! I see you're correcting **NATE WRIGHT'S** most recent test!

That's right, Chip, and he is **FAILING** miserably!

And yet... you seem **HAPPY** about that!

Of **COURSE** I'm happy about it! That's what **I WANTED** to happen!

I... I don't understand.

I told Nate to study Chapter Three! **Then** I tested him on Chapter **TWELVE!**

But... that's totally **UNFAIR!**

Exactly! That's how he'll **LEARN**: by absorbing **DEFEAT** after devastating **DEFEAT!**

You've got to **BREAK** kids' **spirits** while they're young, Chip! Sure, it may seem cruel... but deep down they **LOVE** you for it!

OH, HOW I LOATHE HER.

JUST AN OBSERVATION: THERE WERE NO MATADORS AT THE BATTLE OF BULL RUN.

HI, MRS. SHIPULSKI! NATE "SCOOP" WRIGHT HERE FROM THE P.S. 38 WEEKLY BUGLE!

CAN I INTERVIEW PRINCIPAL NICHOLS?

HE'S IN HIS OFFICE WITH MS. BROWN RIGHT NOW.

OoOOOOH! MR. NICHOLS AND MS. BROWN! HUBBA **HUBBA**!

WAIT! WHAT ARE YOU DOING?

DON'T MAKE IT SOUND AS IF THERE'S SOMETHING **SLEAZY** GOING ON!

A MEETING BETWEEN A TEACHER AND THE PRINCIPAL ISN'T SOME **GOSSIP** ITEM! IT'S A SCHOOL AFFAIR!

AN **AFFAIR**! CAN I QUOTE YOU ON THAT?

NO!

I DIDN'T MEAN IT **THAT** WAY! DON'T WRITE THAT! DON'T USE THE WORD "AFFAIR"!

OKAY, OKAY...

HOW DO YOU SPELL "TRYST"?

IS IT AN "I" OR A "Y"?

SIR, WE HAVE A "CODE RED" OUT HERE.

53

☆ ☆ ☆ ☆ ☆
CELEBRITY
INTER-VIEW!

Here's your host: **CHIP CHIPSON!**

Friends, our guest today is "canine control specialist" **HERMAN SHEPHERD!**

Howdy, Chip.

Herman, isn't "canine control specialist" just a fancy-pants way of saying **"DOG CATCHER"**?

Not at all!

Of course, rounding up strays is **PART** of it, but the most **IMPORTANT** aspect of the job is **PROTECTING THE PUBLIC!**

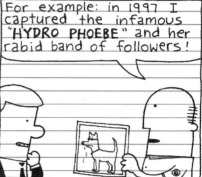

For example: in 1997 I captured the infamous "**HYDRO PHOEBE**" and her rabid band of followers!

I also collared "**Attila the Husky**" in 1999...

...and, in 2001, "**Notorious P.U.G!**"

JL549712

KN753412

Impressive resumé!

Believe me, Chip, they're not **ALL** success stories. **MANY** dogs have slipped through my fingers!

Not **HARDENED CRIMINALS**, mind you, but dogs who nonetheless are **DANGEROUS!** Dogs who are a **MENACE** to everyone around them!

DID YOU HEAR SOMETHING?

HM?

Peirce

CELEBRITY
INTER-VIEW!!

...with your host:
CHIP CHIPSON!

Folks, I'm coming to you live from HEAVEN where I'm chatting with legendary commander-in-chief... ABE LINCOLN!

So, Abe... excited about tomorrow?

Tomorrow?

PRESIDENTS' DAY! It's your birthday celebration!

Actually, Chip, my birthday was LAST week.

Tomorrow is simply an excuse to sell cars and have a three-day weekend.

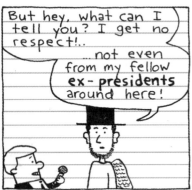

But hey, what can I tell you? I get no respect!.. ...not even from my fellow **ex-presidents** around here!

Like **WASHINGTON** over there! He's always busting my chops because HIS face is on the **QUARTER** and MY face is only on the...

HEY, ABE! "PENNY" FOR YOUR THOUGHTS!

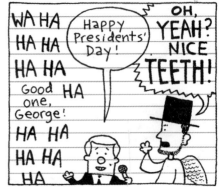

WA HA HA HA HA HA

Happy Presidents' Day!

Good HA one, George!

HA HA HA HA HA

OH, YEAH? NICE TEETH!

NATE!

HI, GORDIE. UM...IS IT OKAY IF I HANG OUT HERE?

KLASSIC KOMIX
OPEN

SURE! WHY **WOULDN'T** IT BE OKAY?

WELL...I JUST WONDERED... BECAUSE OF YOU AND ELLEN...

NATE, YOUR SISTER AND I MAY HAVE BROKEN UP, BUT THAT DOESN'T CHANGE ANYTHING BETWEEN **US!**

REALLY? SO I CAN STILL COME BY TO TALK WITH YOU ABOUT COMICS?

OF COURSE!

AND CAN I STILL HELP YOU WHEN YOU TAKE INVENTORY?

ABSOLUTELY!

AND...

NATE, YOU'LL **ALWAYS** BE WELCOME AT "KLASSIC KOMIX"!

YOU'RE AMONG FRIENDS HERE!

WE NEED A TEACHER PROFILE FOR OUR NEXT EDITION. NATE, DO AN INTERVIEW WITH MR. GALVIN.

WHAT? WHOA!

HOW COME **I'VE** ALWAYS GOT TO DO THE LAME TEACHER INTERVIEWS?

JUST BECAUSE **YOU'RE** THE EDITOR, GINA, THAT DOESN'T MEAN YOU CAN MAKE **ME** DO ALL THE **GRUNT** WORK!

YOU INTERVIEW MR. GALVIN! GIVE **ME** SOMETHING **ELSE** TO DO!

✳ SIGH...✳

OKAY! STOP WHINING! **I'LL** DO THE PIECE ON MR. GALVIN!

YOU CAN DO THE "UP CLOSE AND PERSONAL" WITH DEBBI DALTON.

WHO'S DEBBI DALTON?

SHE'S AN EIGHTH-GRADE GIRL WHO'S TRYING TO GET PERMISSION TO JOIN THE BOYS' WRESTLING TEAM.

...SO THEN I WROTE **ANOTHER** PETITION...

MY PENCIL JUST BROKE.

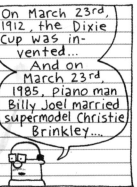

READY... BEGIN.

For each problem in this section, there are five suggested answers. Show your work in the space at the right of the page. Then select which of the five choices is correct.

1. Tom, Dick and Harry are members of the same scout troop and are collecting merit badges. There are 28 merit badges available, divided equally into two types: silver and gold.

Tom has collected 25% of the available merit badges; one of them is gold. Dick has collected 50% of the available merit badges; three of them are silver. Harry has collected 75% of the available merit badges; ·eleven of them are gold.

Harry has collected all the merit badges that Tom has. He has also collected the same gold merit badges that Dick has. But Harry has not collected any of the silver merit badges that Dick has.

Assuming that Tom and Dick do not earn any more merit badges, how many more merit badges must Harry earn to guarantee that he will have the same silver badges (hint: but not necessarily the same NUMBER of badges) as Dick?

RRRRIINNNGGG

NOT ONLY DO I NEED A MATH TUTOR, I MAY ALSO HAVE TO INVEST IN A SPEED-READING COURSE.

☆ ★ ☆ ★ ☆
Celebrity
INTER-VIEW!

with:
BIFF BIFFWELL!

Today, friends, we're chatting with the "month of the month"... MARCH!

Hi, Biff.

So, March... "In like a lion, Out like a lamb," eh?

Yeah. Like I've never heard THAT before.

Now, now, li'l feller. No need to be snippy about it.

PAT PAT!

Hey... HEY! Don't patronize me!

I know what you're thinking, Biff: "Oooh, he's a LAMB! SPRING is here!"

Well, Spring isn't here YET, folks! And I've still got plenty of LION left in me!

But... but you look so DOCILE!

※Sigh...※ Okay, you want proof? I'll give you proof.

RROARR

SHLOX-TV presents: "ARE U A STAR?"

with your host: TY DYSON!

Hi, friends! Did you ever wonder where the next **Britney Spears** or **Nsync** will come from? Well, **WE** did!

So we're searching the country, asking the young people: ARE U A STAR?

I'M a star, Ty!

Well now! What's your name?

I'm ELLEN WRIGHT. I'm 15 years old, and I AM A STAR!

Great! What's your talent?

Talent?

What MAKES you a star, Ellen? Do you sing? Do you dance?

Um... I just want to be famous.

For doing WHAT?

Whatever. I'll do anything!

I'm sorry, Ellen. U ARE **NOT** A STAR!

I... I'm not?

!

SPRING TRAINING

BATTER UP!

THE CRACK OF THE BAT

ROUNDING FIRST...

ROUNDING SECOND...

ROUNDING THIRD...

HEADING FOR HOME

HERE, NATE. PLEASE TAKE THIS OVER TO THE NELSONS' HOUSE.

A DOLL?

IT'S ONE OF ELLEN'S OLD ONES. I TOLD MRS. NELSON SHE COULD HAVE IT FOR HER DAUGHTER.

SPUT!.. I CAN'T BE SEEN WALKING AROUND WITH THIS THING!

I'LL TAKE IT OVER THERE UNDER COVER!

WHATEVER.

HEY, WRIGHT.

HEY, WHAT'S WITH THE BACKPACK, WRIGHT? GOING TO SUMMER SCHOOL?

OooooOH! SUMMER SCHOOL!

I'M NOT GOING TO SUMMER SCHOOL! I'M DOING AN ERRAND!

WHAT ERRAND?

UH... WELL... IT'S...

YOU ARE GOING TO SUMMER SCHOOL! WHAT'S IN HERE, YOUR HOMEWORK?

HEY! DON'T TOUCH THAT!

OKAY, OKAY! YOU DON'T HAVE TO CRY ABOUT IT!

WAAH! WAAH! I NEED A DIAPER CHANGE!

WOULD IT HAVE KILLED YOU TO REMOVE THE BATTERIES?

AAAH, **SPRING!** WHAT A DAY!

SIIIIIGH....

WOOF!

HMM? OH, YOU WANT ME TO THROW THAT BALL, SPITSY? OKAY... JUST ONCE!

GO GET IT!!

I SAID GO **GET** IT, SPITSY!

PANT PANT PANT PANT PANT

GOOD GRAVY. YOU REALLY **ARE** CLUELESS, AREN'T YOU?

PANT PANT PANT PANT PANT

FINE! I'LL GET IT MY**SELF!**

A DOG WHO DOESN'T KNOW HOW TO FETCH! NATE'S RIGHT ABOUT YOU, SPITSY!

HE'S ALWAYS SAYING YOU'RE THE DUMBEST DOG HE'S EVER... !!

AAAAAAHHHH....

SPRING IS HERE!
THE SNOW IS GONE!
WHAT'S THAT GREEN STUFF?
IT'S OUR LAWN!

OUR COATS AND HATS
WE'VE TOSSED ASIDE!
LET'S GRAB OUR BIKES
AND TAKE A RIDE!

WE'LL PLAY SOME CATCH!
WE'LL TOSS SOME 'BEES!
WE'LL SWING SOME BATS!
THE DAY WE'LL SEIZE!

VERY POETIC.

I WROTE IT MYSELF! IT'S CALLED "ODE TO SPRING"!

NOW **I'VE** GOT SOMETHING TO READ.

"I.O.U. ONE FULL DAY OF WORK. ACTUAL DATE AND DETAILS TO BE DETERMINED BY DAD."

YOU WROTE THAT BACK IN JANUARY.

❊SIGH...❊

"OWED TO SPRING"

LITTLE LEAGUE ROSTERS TODAY

PICK UP UNIFORMS HERE

HI, COACH!

WELL! HELLO, GENTS! READY FOR ANOTHER GREAT SEASON?

T-BALL
DOUBLE A
MAJORS →

UH... THAT DEPENDS ON OUR TEAM NAME.

YEAH, WHO'S OUR SPONSOR?

...BECAUSE LAST YEAR WE PLAYED FOR A BEAUTY PARLOR! AND IT WAS MISSPELLED ON OUR UNIFORMS!

YEAH! "CHEEZ LINDA"! WE WERE A LAUGHING-STOCK!

NOT TO WORRY, BOYS! "CHEEZ LINDA" IS NO MORE!

REALLY?

WE HAVE A NEW SPONSOR?

WE CERTAINLY DO! AND THE NAME ISN'T MISSPELLED, EITHER!

...UNFORTUNATELY.

NO!... NO!

CONTINUED NEXT WEEK!!

HOME! HOME!! PLAY AT THE PLATE!

KRAK!

WUMP!

HOLY SMOKES! THIS GUY'S COMIN' FAST!... AND HE'S **HUGE!**

I'M GONNA GET FLATTENED LIKE A PANCAKE!

AND FOR **WHAT**? TO PREVENT A RUN IN A **LITTLE LEAGUE** GAME WE'RE AL-READY LOSING **TEN-ZIP**? IS IT REALLY WORTH IT?

I DON'T THINK SO.

SAFE!

HEY, STAN! YOU FORGOT TO WIPE YOUR FEET!

HA HA HA HA HA HA HA

PLAYING FOR THE "DOORMATS" IS BECOMING A SELF-FULFILLING PROPHECY.

Time Once Again For:

UP-CLOSE ☆ AND ☆ **PERSONAL!**

With your host: BIFF BIFFWELL!

Friends, today my special guest is "yearbook inscription expert" **ALAN ANNUAL!**

"Warm regards," Biff!

Alan, what **IS** a "yearbook inscription expert"?

Biff, we've **ALL** been asked to sign yearbooks for classmates or teachers!

✶chuckle!✶ So true!

But we don't always know **WHAT TO WRITE!** That's where **I** come in!

I help folks find **JUST THE RIGHT WORDS** for a PAL...

See you this summer, ol' buddy ol' pal!

...or merely an **ACQUAINTANCE!**

Have a nice summer.

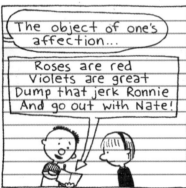

The object of one's affection...

Roses are red
Violets are great
Dump that jerk Ronnie
And go out with Nate!

...or perhaps a respected mentor!

Thou "ART" a great teacher! (Ha Ha!)

But Alan...what if you find yourself signing the yearbook of someone you **HATE**?

It **CAN** be done, Biff!

The trick is finding the perfect phrase! There truly **IS** an inscription for every occasion!

Mrs. Godfrey—I can't tell you how much I enjoyed your class this year.

Nate

Biff & Chip "**ON SAFARI**"

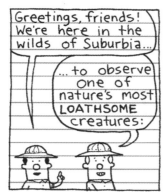

Greetings, friends! We're here in the wilds of Suburbia...

...to observe one of nature's most LOATHSOME creatures:

...the SIXTH-GRADE SOCIAL STUDIES TEACHER!

There she is, Biff! But... who's that WITH her?

That's a common schoolchild: "Academius Downtroddenus".

He looks EXHAUST-ED, Biff!

Oh, he IS! He's been her PRISONER since September!

SEPTEMBER? EGAD! Why doesn't she just EAT him and be DONE with it?

The schoolchild isn't FOOD for her, Chip! He's her AMUSEMENT! She screams at him, bosses him around, and brain-washes him with USELESS TRIVIA!

But... that's so CRUEL!

There IS hope, though, Chip. NATURE'S TIMETABLE is taking over!

See? She's going into SUMMER HIBER-NATION!

...And "Academius Downtroddenus" can ESCAPE! RUN! RUN!

RRRRIINNNGG

SNACK BAR?

SNACK BAR!

I'M STARVING!

OKAY, I'VE GOT... HMM... I'VE GOT $3.55...

A HOT DOG IS $1.75... A SODA IS 85 CENTS... ICE CREAM IS $1.20...

DO I HAVE ENOUGH TO BUY ALL THREE? LET'S SEE HERE...

$1.75 PLUS .85... THAT'S... UH... THAT'S $2.60... PLUS... UMMM...

WAIT A MINUTE! WHAT AM I DOING?

WHAT ARE YOU DOING?

MATH! I'M DOING MATH!

I'M DOING MATH! DURING SUMMER VACATION!!

THIS IS WRONG! THIS IS SO WRONG!

HERE. YOU FIGURE IT OUT.

HE'S A MAN OF PRINCIPLE

✳ sigh... ✳

KRAK!

YES!

BAG OF CHIPS AND AN ORANGE SODA, PLEASE.

THE MOST EXCITING PLAY IN BASEBALL:

A FOUL BALL THAT LANDS NEAR THE SNACK BOOTH!

Time Once Again For...

BIFF & CHIP...

ON SAFARI!

What are we tracking today, Biff?

Chip, it's the common 6th-grade social studies teacher!

But... the school year is OVER!

EXACTLY! We'll be observing her during her SUMMER HIBERNATION! Oop! There she IS!

Does she actually hibernate, Biff?

Not LITERALLY! But she does a lot of lying around! She needs to REST!

Rest? Is she SICK?

If by "sick" you mean "sadistic and needlessly cruel," then... YES, Chip! Yes, she IS sick!

HEY! This Frisbee almost HIT me! JERK!

She's just spent an entire school year BULLYING and PERSE-CUTING her students! Making IMPOSSIBLE demands! PUNISHING them INDISCRIMINATELY!

Say, that DOES sound tiring!

It IS, mi amigo! Teachers burn a LOT of calories!

That's why she needs to BULK UP! To ensure that she's ready for another grueling year, she needs to add FAT to her body! LOTS of fat!

JUMBO BANANA SPLIT WITH DOUBLE FUDGE!

SHE'S "SUPER-SIZING"!

SHOPPING BAG

SNACK BAG

GRAB BAG

GARBAGE BAG

CHIP

GYM BAG

SPEED BAG

HEAVY BAG

AAAAAAAHH

BEAN BAG

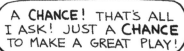

DOGS ARE SO MUCH SMARTER THAN CATS.

OH, PLEASE...

LET'S NOT HAVE **THIS** CONVERSATION AGAIN.

IT'S **TRUE**! IT'S A WELL-DOCUMENTED **FACT**!

DID YOU EVER HEAR ABOUT A **CAT** RESCUING SOMEONE FROM A BURNING BUILDING? CAN A **CAT** BE A GUIDE FOR A BLIND PERSON?

NOPE. WHEN A JOB TAKES BRAINS, THEY ASK A **DOG** TO DO IT!

THAT'S **YOUR** OPINION! DOGS ARE **NOT** SMARTER THAN CATS!

THEY **ARE**, AND I'LL **PROVE** IT!

SPITSY! HERE, BOY!

SPITSY, GO INTO THE GARAGE AND BRING ME MY SOCCER CLEATS.

PANT PANT PANT

WATCH **THIS**!

ZIP!

WAM!

THAT "SMARTS"!

YOU DUMB DOG.

THERE!

PHYSICAL FITNESS MERIT BADGE, HERE I COME!

YOU'RE MY WITNESS, OKAY, FRANCIS? YOU'LL ATTEST TO THE FACT THAT I CLIMBED A FIFTEEN-FOOT ROPE!

YUP!

UP I GO!

YOU'RE HALFWAY!

OOF! GRUNT!

ALMOST THERE!

HM?

FWIP! FWIP!

YAAAH!

HOW'RE YOU DOING ON YOUR KNOT-TYING MERIT BADGE?

OW

WHERE ARE WE GOING?

SCHOOL!

SCHOOL?

AH! ISN'T THAT A BEAUTIFUL SIGHT?

P.S.

HAVE
SUM

P.S. 38! EMPTY! LIFELESS! IN MOTHBALLS 'TIL AFTER LABOR DAY!

YEAH... SO?

SO? SO SAVOR IT, TEDDY! DRINK IT IN, MAN!

IT'S LIKE A LION THAT'S LOST ALL ITS TEETH! IT HAS NO CONTROL OVER US DURING THE SUMMER! IT'S **POWERLESS!**

HELLO, BOYS.

! !

SINCE YOU'RE HERE, YOU CAN HELP ME CARRY SOME HEAVY BOXES TO MY CAR.

"DRINK IT IN, MAN."

OH, HOW I HATE HER.

YOU'RE HITTIN' 'EM RIGHT **AT** ME! GIVE ME SOME **TOUGH** ONES!

OKAY, OKAY.

Krak!

!

SLAM!

WHAT'S YOUR **PROBLEM**, KID? YOU JUST SCREWED UP OUR **GAME!**

S-SORRY. I WAS JUST TRYING TO CATCH MY BALL.

THIS BALL?

WE'LL HELP YOU CATCH IT!

TOUGH ENOUGH FOR YOU?

MMRMPH.

HERE COMES THAT NEW GIRL.

OOH! LET'S TALK TO HER!

GOOD LUCK. SHE WON'T TALK TO **ANY**ONE. SHE SEEMS KIND OF STUCK-UP.

I'LL BET SHE'S JUST **SHY!** SHE DOESN'T TALK TO ANYONE BECAUSE NOBODY TALKS TO **HER!**

AND THERE'S NOTHING LIKE A **DOG** TO GET A CONVERSATION GOING!

SPITSY GOES UP TO HER, WAGS HIS TAIL... THEN **I** SWOOP IN AND CHARM HER **SOCKS OFF!**

WAG WAG WAG WAG WAG

GOT THAT, SPITSY? GO GET HER! GO SAY HI!

WHAT'S HAPPEN-ING?

CAN'T TELL. THERE'S A TREE IN THE WAY.

...BUT THAT'S ENOUGH TIME. I'M **GOIN' IN!**

HEL-**LO!**

IS THIS YOUR DOG?

WELL... **PRACTICALLY.** I DOG-SIT FOR HIM, YOU SEE, AND...

HE JUST **THREW UP ON MY FEET!**

AS PROMISED, HER SOCKS ARE OFF.

YOU SPAZ.

the COMPE- TITION

10 FT

CANNONBALL

JACK-KNIFE

SWAN DIVE

FLIP

CORKSCREW

$"Money Matters" $ $
with your host
BIFF BIFFWELL
and special guest...

CONSUMER REPORTER
CELINE PAYCHEK!!

Hi, Celine!

Nice to be here, Biff!

Celine, it's BACK-TO-SCHOOL time again! Any shopping tips for parents trying to save a few pennies?

Absolutely, Biff!

DON'T be fooled by all the so-called "SALES"! That's the stuff the stores WANT you to buy!

Instead, check out the items marked "CLEARANCE"!

Your 11-year-old son might want a backpack like everyone ELSE's, but WHY PAY MORE?

Here's a perfectly good "Pinky the Pony" pack for HALF THE COST!

...And Biff, who needs some fancy-pants NOTE-BOOK with all those pockets, compartments, and zippers?

This plain brown binder is a STEAL, and the water damage is MINIMAL!

Then, of course, there's the matter of CLOTHES! Your children might beg you for "NICE" clothes that "FIT" and "LOOK GOOD"! ...AND, might I add, cost an ARM and a LEG!

Why pay through the nose? What's more important: some pair of pants your kid's going to outgrow... OR SAVING YOUR PRECIOUS, HARD-EARNED MONEY??

$ $ $

WE'LL TAKE 'EM!

SIGH

CLE

CLEARAN

I'VE **GOT** IT! **PROOF POSITIVE** THAT DOGS ARE BETTER THAN CATS!

AGAIN?

SEE THIS BOOK? IT'S ALL ABOUT **DOGS** THAT WERE **HEROES** IN **WARS**!

CANINE COURAGE

LOOK! DOGS THAT DELIVERED MESSAGES BEHIND ENEMY LINES! DOGS THAT RESCUED WOUNDED SOLDIERS! DOGS THAT SNIFFED OUT BOOBY TRAPS AND LAND MINES!

THAT SAYS IT ALL, FRANCIS! DOGS HAVE ANSWERED THE CALL IN THE HEAT OF **BATTLE!**

✻CHUCKLE!✻ HOW DO YOU THINK **PICKLES** HERE WOULD DO IN A **WAR**?

FSSSSSST!

RROWR!!

I THINK SHE'D HAVE HER OWN REGIMENT!

I HATE CATS.

"EXTREME" SPORTS ARE THE WAVE OF THE FUTURE, RIGHT?

I GUESS.

HALF-PIPE, STREET LUGE, BUNGEE JUMPING... TWENTY YEARS AGO, NOBODY HAD EVEN **HEARD** OF THIS STUFF!

...SO **I** FIGURED: WHY NOT INVENT A **NEW** EXTREME SPORT?

ROLLER-VAULTING!

THAT LOOKS DANGEROUS.

OF **COURSE** IT'S DANGEROUS!

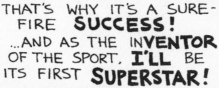

THAT'S WHY IT'S A SURE-FIRE **SUCCESS**! ...AND AS THE IN**VENTOR** OF THE SPORT, **I'LL** BE ITS FIRST **SUPERSTAR!**

BEFORE YOU KNOW IT, YOU'LL BE SEEING ME ON **TV!**

A LOCAL BOY IS LUCKY TO BE ALIVE TODAY AFTER HE...

THERE YOU ARE!

Peirce

SPROOINNGG...

ZOINNNG!

WHAM!

COULDN'T YOU JUST GRAB THE FRISBEE FROM THE TOP OF THE LADDER?

THIS WAY IS MORE FUN.

☆★☆★☆★☆
BACK-TO-SCHOOL
"DO"
and
"DON'T"
GUIDE!!

by: Nate Wright

DO: Ride the bus!!

PAR-TAY!

Dang! Turn off the 'N Sync!

SCHOOL DISTRICT 3

DON'T: Get driven to school by a parent!

Remember to use those "handi-wipes" after lunch!

I love you, son!

DO: Get back-to-school **supplies**!

This notebook holds 6 candy bars AND a juice box!

Cool!

DON'T: Get a back-to-school **haircut**!

What's with the hat?

None o' your beeswax.

DO: Talk to "new kids"!

Well hel-**LO** there!

Can I show you around?

DON'T: Talk to new teachers!

...And what's your **APPROACH** to teaching math?

What a BROWN-NOSE!

Let's wedgie him later!

DO: Catch up on all the gossip!

Hey, Dave! How's Sharon?

She... I... We... ♪ SOB! ♪

Oh. Sorry, man.

DON'T: Ask Kevin Gladchuk "how was your summer?"

Funny you should ask. I have here some photos...

DO: Stand up to 7th-grade bullies!

DON'T! DON'T!!

HEY, GUYS! JOIN IN!

TRASH

12

Can **YOU** tell the difference between an **OLD TEACHER** and a **YOUNG TEACHER?**

here are some **TIPS!**

OLD TEACHER: Spends every free moment in the faculty lounge!

Mr. Galvin! I need help with my homework! Mr. Galvin?

knock knock

`SPORTS`

YOUNG TEACHER: Prefers to be "accessible" to the students!

...Yes, but on page 785 of "Harry Potter and the Order of the Phoenix," I noticed that...

OLD TEACHER: textbook!

Read Chapter 12, answer the questions at the end, then sit quietly until the bell rings.

YOUNG TEACHER: multimedia!

...and after we finish our papier-mâché puppets, there's a **REALLY** cool website I want to show you!

OLD TEACHER: Will NOT deviate from lesson plan... *NO MATTER WHAT!*

I'm confused. Can you explain Question #4?

No, I'm afraid not. There's no time for that.

Moving on to Question #5...

YOUNG TEACHER: Likes to remain "flexible" in the classroom!

Can we watch a video?

I hadn't planned on it, but... **SURE!**

Which video? Suggestions, people?

OLD TEACHER: Has eerie, all-seeing, all-knowing radar!

Stop it.

Stop what?

You know what.

Dang!

YOUNG TEACHER: Has no clue that you're busting on him!

※AHEM!※

Hey, gang! Who wants a snack?

I NEED A NICKNAME.

ALL THE GREAT FOOTBALL PLAYERS HAVE NICKNAMES!

YOU KNOW, LIKE DEION SANDERS IS "PRIME TIME".. JEROME BETTIS IS "THE BUS"..

...BUT I CAN'T THINK OF A GOOD NICKNAME FOR MYSELF!

MAYBE SOME-THING WILL COME TO ME.

HEY! SPITSY! WHAT ARE YOU DOING?

!

HEY! GET OFF ME! GET OFF!

SPITSY!! LEMME GO!!

RRRRR

RRRIP!

HOW ABOUT "FLASH"?

JUST FIND ME A TOWEL.

HI, MRS. SHIPULSKI.

HELLO, NATE.

I'M HERE TO SEE PRINCIPAL NICHOLS.

YOU'LL HAVE TO WAIT. ARTUR IS IN WITH HIM RIGHT NOW.

!! ARTUR !!

MM-HM. HAVE A SEAT.

WELL, **WELL!** WHO WOULD'VE **THUNK** IT!

ARTUR IS IN THE **PRINCIPAL'S** OFFICE! I GUESS **MR. PERFECT** MUST HAVE **SCREWED UP!**

PRETTY **QUIET** IN THERE!

✻CHUCKLE!✻ ARTUR MUST BE SQUIRMING IN HIS SEAT WHILE NICHOLS GIVES HIM THE **HAIRY EYEBALL!**

WONDERFUL JOB, ARTUR! IT'S BEEN **THIRTY YEARS** SINCE ONE OF OUR STUDENTS EARNED THE CITYWIDE "GOOD CITIZENSHIP" AWARD!

YOU'VE MADE US VERY PROUD, SON!

WE'LL PUT YOUR PLAQUE IN THE DISPLAY CASE IMMEDIATELY!

THANK YOU, SIR.

OH, HOW I HATE HIM.

NEXT?

WHAT'RE YOU READING?

"GARFIELD." ...WHO, BY THE WAY, IS A **CAT**!

SO?

SO, THERE ARE A LOT MORE **CATS** IN CARTOONS AND COMICS THAN **DOGS**, I'LL BET!

I THINK NOT.

HEATHCLIFF! KRAZY KAT! FLESHY! TOM!

SNOOPY! DROOPY! GOOFY! MARMADUKE! DOGBERT!

BUCKY KATT! TOP CAT! FELIX THE CAT! CATBERT!

OFFISSA PUP! DEPUTY DAWG! SCOOBY DOO! PLUTO! ASTRO! OTTO!

BILL THE CAT! SYLVESTER THE CAT!

JOSIE AND THE PUSSYCATS! THE **ARISTOCATS**!

UH... OK... UMM.... LET'S SEE HERE...

RUFF!

YES!... **YES**!! DENNIS THE MENACE'S DOG IS NAMED **RUFF**! **HA**!

WAY TO GO, SPITSY!

DOGGONE IT.

NATE!

HM?

MAYBE YOU COULD STOP PLAYING **TABLE FOOTBALL** AND WORK ON OUR **REPORT**, FOOL!

DON'T CALL ME "FOOL", GINA! I'M NOT A FOOL!

ASK ANYONE! ASK THE TEACHERS! ASK THE GUIDANCE COUNSELOR!

THEY ALL SAY THE SAME THING: I'VE GOT UNLIMITED POTENTIAL AND COULD DO OUTSTANDING WORK IF I APPLIED MYSELF!

THEY WOULDN'T WASTE THEIR TIME TELLING ME TO DO BETTER IF THEY DIDN'T THINK I **COULD**!

IN OTHER WORDS, YOU'RE A DISAPPOINTMENT TO EVERYONE.

EXACTLY! THAT **PROVES** HOW SMART I AM!

MY HEAD HURTS.

YOU'RE PROBABLY WORKING TOO HARD.

161

HERE COMES MY PET PROJECT!

CHESTER?

CHESTER IS YOUR PET PROJECT?

THAT'S RIGHT! I'M GOING TO REFORM HIM!

REFORM HIM? WHY?

LOOK, EVERYONE'S AFRAID OF THE GUY, RIGHT?

...BUT HE MUST HAVE SOME GOOD IN HIM! NOBODY'S BORN THAT MEAN!

HE ACTS LIKE A BULLY BECAUSE NOBODY'S EVER BEEN NICE TO HIM! IF I TREAT HIM LIKE A FRIEND, HE'LL STOP BEING SUCH A THUG!

IT SAYS SO RIGHT HERE IN THIS BOOK!

PAT PAT

CHESTER, MY MAN!

WHAM!

"UNDERSTANDING BULLIES"

HE'S A WORK IN PROGRESS.

163

The GAME FACE

POW!

SAME OLD SAME OLD.

WHAT DO YOU MEAN?

ALL YOU EVER DRAW IS MEAN CARTOONS ABOUT OUR TEACHERS!

HEE HEE! YEAH, I KNOW! IT'S MY SPECIALTY!

CARTOONS DON'T HAVE TO BE **CRUEL** ALL THE TIME! TRY DRAWING A **NICE** CARTOON ABOUT A TEACHER!

A NICE CARTOON?

OKAY, I ACCEPT YOUR CHALLENGE! I'LL DRAW A NICE CARTOON ABOUT MRS. GODFREY!

I CAN DO THIS.

I... CAN... ✳GASP!✳ DO...THIS... I... I...

BWA HA HA HA HA

YOU CALL THAT **NICE?**

I **MEANT** IT TO BE! I WAS **THINKING** NICE, BUT THEN MY DRAWING HAND TOOK OVER!

MY MIND WAS STRONG, BUT MY FLESH WAS WEAK!

YOU'RE HALF RIGHT.

Time again for the adventures of

SUPERDAD!

The world's ONLY superhero with a slight paunch!

...AND

MEGA-TEEN!

sigh...

She fights crime! AND really bad hair days!

One fine day...

Come, Mega-teen! It's time to...

← dramatic pause

RUN SOME ERRANDS!

To the DAD-MOBILE!

Oooh! Superdad! Can I drive the Dad-mobile? I've got my learner's permit!

Well...

Five minutes later...

Why aren't we moving?

Try putting it in gear, Mega-teen.

NO, NO! Put it in REVERSE! REVERSE!

Oopsy.

CRASH!

What are you DOING, Mega-teen?

Putting it in reverse.

That's the RADIO!

Okay, I'm backing out of the driveway...

LOOK OUT!

Screeee

WHY DON'T YOU LET ME DRIVE, ELLEN...

WHO PUT THAT MAILBOX THERE?

WRIGHT

Time for **BIFF** and **CHIP....** *ON SAFARI!!*

G'day, mates!

In Nature, Chip, "OPPOSITES ATTRACT"!

Right, Biff! Let's take a look at the unlikely friendship...

...between the lumbering 6th grade Social Studies teacher...

Or, in scientific jargon, "Bad Breathius Hideosa".

...AND the hyperactive, eager-to-please TEACHER'S PET!

"Boot-Lickius Obedientius".

What makes this bizarre relationship WORK, Chip?

Biff, each of these creatures plays its role PERFECTLY!

The TEACHER is a sluggish creature whose instinct is to do NOTHING!

... while the PET lives to do her BIDDING!

Shoo, fly!

When she needs something done, he DOES it! When she needs something fetched, he FETCHES it!

LOOK at her! She barely has to MOVE!

But WHY does the pet STAY in such a one-sided relationship?

Indeed, Biff: what's in it for HIM?

COLONIAL TIME

YOU MAKE ME SICK.

WELCOME PLAYERS! TRI-COUNTY SCHOLASTIC **CHESS** TOURNAMENT

REGISTER HERE →

HOW'RE YOU DOING SO FAR?

I WON MY FIRST MATCH!

PAT?

PAT BLEVINS OF AMESBURY MIDDLE SCHOOL VERSUS NATE WRIGHT OF P.S. 38!

HMM... THIS GUY DOESN'T LOOK TOO TOUGH!

STILL, HE'S IN THE WINNER'S BRACKET, SO MAYBE HE'S... HMM? HE'S **WHISTLING!**

WELL, EITHER HE'S NOT TAKING THE MATCH SERIOUSLY, OR... ?? WHA-?... NOW HE'S EATING **CHEEZ DOODLES!**

CRUNCH MUNCH

...AND WHAT SORT OF WEIRD MOVE IS **THAT**?... DOES THIS KID HAVE ANY IDEA WHAT HE'S **DOING**?

!! NOW I'VE SEEN **EVERYTHING!** HE'S READING A **COMIC BOOK!**

THIS KID'S **CLUELESS!** I'M GONNA BLOW HIM OFF THE BOARD!

HELLO? IS HE GOING TO **DO** SOMETHING? DOES HE EVEN **KNOW** IT'S **HIS MOVE?**

CHECKMATE

!

HOW'RE YOU DOING SO FAR?

OH, SHUT UP.

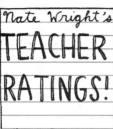

Nate Wright's

TEACHER RATINGS!

Where Do **YOUR** Teachers Rate in the **HALL OF SHAME?**

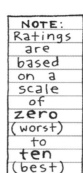

NOTE: Ratings are based on a scale of **zero** (worst) to **ten** (best)

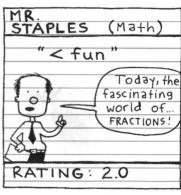

MR. STAPLES (Math)

"< fun"

Today, the fascinating world of... FRACTIONS!

RATING: 2.0

MRS. BRINDLE (LIFE SKILLS)

"A recipe for disaster"

...and after 20 minutes, our "johnny-cake" is done!

RATING: 1.3

MS. LA CHANCE (French)

"Ooh La Loser"

Let the words RRRRROLL off your tongue!

RATING: 0.8

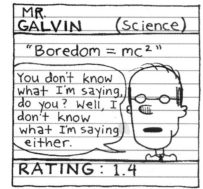

MR. GALVIN (Science)

"Boredom = mc^2"

You don't know what I'm saying, do you? Well, I don't know what I'm saying either.

RATING: 1.4

MR. ALDRIDGE (Computer Lab)

Press "escape"

Wait. Wait. That wasn't supposed to... okay, wait. Wait.

tik tak tik tak tik tak

RATING: 1.1

MRS. GODFREY (Social Studies)

"Oh, the humanity."

I summon thee, hounds of Satan!

RATING: -3,000,000

DO YOU ACTUALLY EXPECT ME TO PUT THIS IN THE DISPLAY CASE?

THINK OF IT AS A PUBLIC SERVICE!

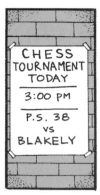

CHESS
TOURNAMENT
TODAY

3:00 PM

P.S. 38
vs
BLAKELY

WHAT A REVOLTING DEVELOPMENT! HERE I SIT, PLAYING AGAINST THEIR SECOND-BEST PLAYER!

...WHILE ARTUR GETS TO PLAY AGAINST THEIR NUMBER **ONE!**

THAT SHOULD BE ME OVER THERE.

BEFORE "CHESS BOY" CAME ALONG, **I** WAS OUR TEAM'S TOP PLAYER!

BUT... **WAIT** A SEC! WHAT IF ARTUR **LOSES**?

IF ARTUR LOSES **HIS** MATCH AND I WIN **MINE**, I'LL BE BACK ON **TOP!** I'LL BE NUMBER ONE!

SOUNDS LIKE A PLAN! I'LL JUST POLISH THIS GUY OFF AND...

CHECKMATE

CHECKMATE

GET SMART. PLAY CHESS.

VERY FUNNY.

Tired of the same old superheroes? Meet...

SUPERDAD!

...the world's **ONLY** bald superhero with a slight paunch!

FASTER than the average 46-year-old!...

GASP!

PANT! HEAVE!

Mommy, is that man having a heart attack?

STRONGER than a jar of sweet mini gherkins!...

YES! **GOT** it!

Now that's **MUSCLE**!

But you used vise grips!

MORE POWERFUL than... than... uh... well, we'll come back to that one.

ZZZZZZONK!

Able to **LEAP** to conclusions in a single bound!

Who ate the last doughnut? It was **YOU**, wasn't it, **NATE**?

Yes, he's **SUPER-DAD!!** Defender of the defenseless! Protector of the weak! Fearless guardian of the...

— DING DONG!

YOU answer that.

HI, THERE! MAY I SPEAK TO THE HEAD OF THE HOUSEHOLD ABOUT VINYL SIDING?

I'M NOT HERE.

NATE!

HUH?

HAVE YOU EVER HEARD OF A LITTLE SOMETHING CALLED **BODY LANGUAGE**?

UH...I GUESS SO.

WELL, **YOURS** IS **AWFUL**! YOU'RE **SLOUCHING**! YOU'RE ALL **SLUMPED OVER**!

A STUDENT IN **MY** CLASS NEEDS TO LOOK **ALERT**! YOU NEED TO SHOW ME YOU'RE **READY TO LEARN**!

PSST! NATE! I CAN HELP YOU WITH THAT!

HMM?

YANK!

NOW **THAT'S** MORE **LIKE** IT!

BEHOLD THE POWER OF THE WEDGIE.

TIME! GAME OVER, GENTS!

HONK

WHAT'S WITH YOU?

WHATTA YA MEAN?

WHY DO YOU LOOK SO **MAD**?

WE **WON**!

I KNOW.

BUT I'VE STILL GOT MY **GAME FACE** ON!

I SPENT ALL **DAY** GETTING PSYCHED UP FOR THIS GAME! I **WILLED** MY FACE INTO A MASK OF COMPETITIVE INTENSITY!

I CAN'T JUST **TURN OFF** THAT INTENSITY LIKE A...

HE**LLO**, LADIES!

...LIKE A HOSE.

WHATCHA GOT?

AN OLD YEARBOOK!

OVER IN THE REFERENCE STACKS THEY HAVE COPIES OF EVERY YEARBOOK IN THE SCHOOL'S **HISTORY!**

COOL!

THIS ONE'S FROM TWENTY YEARS AGO! IT'S TOTALLY **HILARIOUS!**

QUIET PLEASE

IS THAT... MR. **GALVIN?**

HEE HEE! YUP! HE WAS ACTUALLY **YOUNG** ONCE!

WOW! LOOK AT MRS. BELLAMY!

✶ SNICKER! ✶ TWENTY YEARS AND **FORTY POUNDS** AGO!

QU PLE

HEY! IS MR. ROSA IN THERE?

LET'S SEE...

FLIP FLIP

MMPH! NICE **HAIR!**

✶ SNORT! ✶ NICE **DISCO** SHIRT!

HA HA HA

HA HEE HEE

HA HA

HELLO, BOYS.

WA HA HA A HA HA HA HA HA HA HA

THIS IS WHY, DURING FREE PERIODS, I TEND TO STAY IN MY CLASSROOM WITH THE DOOR LOCKED.

HA HA HA HA HA HA HA HA HE'S A DISCO INFERNO! A HA

G is for the Gruesome class she teaches;

O is for Obese, it's plain to see.

D is for her favorite Dinner: leeches.

F, the grade she gives most Frequently.

R is for her Rages never-ending;

E, her Evil Eye which never blinks.

Y is for my Youth which I am spending

sitting in detention.

MAN, THIS STINKS.

UP-CLOSE
and
PERSONAL!

with your host:
BIFF BIFFWELL!

Greetings once again, friends! Today's guest is Halloween pumpkin **JACK O'LANTERN!** What's up, Jack?

You da man, Biff!

I must say, Jack, you're looking quite **FIERCE** today!

Well, I'm one of the lucky ones!

After all, we pumpkins can't carve **OURSELVES!** Someone **GAVE** me this face!

...And, happily enough, I ended up with a "classic" Halloween expression! **OTHERS** aren't so fortunate!

Really?

Absolutely! And once you've been carved, you're **STUCK** with whatever face you get!

We call those unlucky gourds "**JERK**-o-lanterns"!

Oop! Here comes one now!

The poor sap.

Try not to stare.

Hi, fellers!

HI, MR. EUSTIS! CAN N.F.T. YARD-CARE RAKE YOUR LEAVES?

NOT THIS YEAR, NATE. I NEED THE EXERCISE!

HMM... DO YOU REALLY THINK THAT'S WISE?

WHAT DO YOU MEAN?

RAKING LEAVES IS HARD WORK, MR. EUSTIS! REAL CARDIO-VASCULAR STUFF!

AFTER AN HOUR OR TWO, YOU'LL BE PERSPIRING... SHORT OF BREATH... YOUR CHEST AND ARMS WILL FEEL TIGHT...

...AND SUDDENLY, YOU'LL FIND YOURSELF WONDERING: AM I HAVING A HEART ATTACK?

...SO YOU'LL CALL YOUR DOCTOR, WHO WILL CHECK YOU INTO THE HOSPITAL FOR A COMPLETE BATTERY OF TESTS!

TOTAL COST TO YOU: TWELVE, THIRTEEN HUNDRED DOLLARS!

...OR, YOU CAN JUST HIRE US FOR FIFTY!

NICE SALES PITCH!

JUST A BUSINESSMAN DOING MY JOB!

Hey, TRIVIA BUFFS!
Test your Knowledge!
TAKE the...
Mrs. GODFREY
TRUE or FALSE QUIZ!

TRUE or FALSE:
In her high school yearbook, Mrs. Godfrey listed her "hobbies" as "unprovoked rage" and "lunch."

what are YOU lookin' at? HUH?

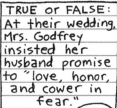
TRUE or FALSE:
At their wedding, Mrs. Godfrey insisted her husband promise to "love, honor, and cower in fear."

Whatever you say, dear!

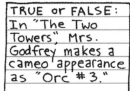
TRUE or FALSE:
In "The Two Towers," Mrs. Godfrey makes a cameo appearance as "Orc #3."

AAARRGHHH
Gandalf! HELP!

TRUE or FALSE:
Mrs. Godfrey's breath has been classified as a "weapon of mass destruction."

tuna
meat loaf
cheese
cabbage
mold
rotten eggs

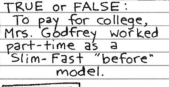
TRUE or FALSE:
To pay for college, Mrs. Godfrey worked part-time as a "Slim-Fast "before" model.

TRUE or FALSE:
Mrs. Godfrey's unpublished autobiography is entitled "Forever Torpid."

CHIPS

CHECK IT OUT! TRUE OR FALSE?

! !

TRUE.
So TRUE.
AGAIN?
DETENTION

207

SHLOX-TV presents:

:25

25 minutes of 6th-grade Social Studies!

Events occur in real time

8:30

Goooood morning, Mrs. Godfrey!

Shut up and sit down.

8:32

Surprise quiz, people.

But... you said we were watching a filmstrip!

Hence the term "surprise" quiz.

8:37

Um... this quiz is on stuff we haven't even studied yet.

Well, you should have read ahead.

8:42

Hand 'em in.

But... I'm only half done!

Ask me if I half-care.

8:44

Okay, now I'm going to drone on and on in a mind-numbing monotone about an obscure and meaningless historical event.

On March 1st, 1790, Congress authorized a decennial U.S. census, meaning that the

8:49

and it was at that point, in 1795, that the U.S. decided to purchase peace from the Algerian pirates who were holding 115 sailors hostage, and follow this

8:53

Are you chewing GUM?

It's a cough drop. I have a cold.

Gum-chewing in class is FORBIDDEN!

8:54

But it isn't gum! It's...

Are you SASSING me, Mister?

No, I...

NO ONE SASSES ME!

PRINCIPAL

TICK TICK TICK TICK

Peirce

WHEW!

THAT SNOW IS **HEAVY**!

YOU SHOVELED?

OF **COURSE** I SHOVELED! I WANTED TO GET IT CLEARED OFF RIGHT AWAY!

WOW!

WHAT A SURPRISE! THAT'S VERY THOUGHTFUL OF YOU, NATE!

I APPRECIATE YOUR HARD WORK! SHOVELING THE DRIVEWAY IS A BIG JOB!

DRIVEWAY?

WHY THE HECK WOULD I SHOVEL THE **DRIVE**WAY?

I SHOVELED THE **POND**!

PRIORITIES, DAD! PRIORITIES!

"Welcome once again to... "MILD WORLD of SPORTS" with BIFF BIFFWELL!

Hello, friends! Today we'll be treated to a gala FIGURE SKATING exhibition! Here to provide commentary is TODD ZAMBONI!

HI Biff!

Todd, who's our first skater?

It's ELLEN WRIGHT, unveiling a new program!

CLAP!
CLAP!
CLAP!
CLAP!
CLAP!

...And here comes her first jump!

She INVENTED that move! It's called the "ugly duckling"!

And now... a combination jump!

Yes, it's a combination of CLUMSINESS and INEPTITUDE!

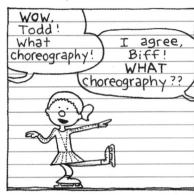

WOW, Todd! What choreography!

I agree, Biff! WHAT choreography??

Like all good routines, this one tells a story!

Right, Biff! It's the story of an awkward girl who can't skate very well!

I must say, Todd, Ellen has some UNUSUAL moves!

She sure does! There's no telling what she'll do NEXT!

!

THAT'S A MOVE I'VE NEVER SEEN BEFORE

DAD, IT'S **FREEZING** OUT HERE!

IT'S **BRISK**, THAT'S ALL! WE CAN'T LET **THAT** STOP US!

WE HAVE A FAMILY FOOTBALL GAME **EVERY** THANKSGIVING WEEKEND! IT'S **TRADITIONAL!**

TRADITIONS ARE IMPORTANT, SON! DOING THE SAME THINGS, IN THE SAME WAY, YEAR AFTER YEAR...THAT HAS **MEANING!**

BUT THERE'S **ICE** ON THE LAWN!

ICE, SCHMICE! KICK OFF!

DOOF!

LET'S HEAR IT FOR TRADITION!!

ZZOOOP!

!

WAM!

YOU'RE HERE EVERY YEAR ABOUT THIS TIME, AREN'T YOU?

EMERG

◄ ADMITTIN

◄ X-RAY

◄ PHYSICAL

Peirce

BEEP
BEEP
BEEP
BOOP
BOOP
BEEP
BEEP

YEAH, IS THIS METEOROLOGIST WINK SUMMERS? YO, WINK. NATE WRIGHT HERE.

WHAT'S UP WITH YOUR **FORECAST**, WINK? YOU SAID WE'D HAVE **BELOW-FREEZING TEMPERATURES ALL WEEKEND!**

INSTEAD, IT'S **40 DEGREES** OUTSIDE, IN CASE YOU DIDN'T KNOW!

WHY AM I UPSET? BECAUSE I WANT TO PLAY **HOCKEY**, THAT'S WHY! AND THE LOCAL **SKATING POND** IS A BIG, WET **PUDDLE!**

THE NEXT TIME YOU PROMISE ME **ICE**, WINK, I WANT TO SEE **ICE!** WHAT DO YOU SAY TO **THAT?**

THAT WAS COLD.

BIFF BIFFWELL, hard-hitting interviewer, *chats with...* consumer reporter **CELINE PAYCHEK**!

Celine, our mailbag is **FULL** of letters asking: what should I get **DAD** for Christmas... on a **LIMITED BUDGET**??

Good question, Biff!

High-end gifts for Dad, like the "Reach-A-Round Razor" for pesky back hair...

...or the "Snak-o-belt"® are simply too **EXPENSIVE** for most buyers!

bzzzz

Instead, I advise shoppers to **WAIT** until the **LAST MINUTE**! Buy that gift for Dad today or tomorrow, when the prices **DROP**!

So there are bargains to be found, eh?

There sure are, Biff! However, there **IS** a downside!

Most of the **GOOD** merchandise has been picked over! Shopping for Dad at the last minute means you **MIGHT** have **LESS** to **CHOOSE FROM**!

CLEARA

I CAN AFFORD **BOTH** THE COWBOY HAT **AND** THE "BUNS OF STEEL" VIDEO!

HE'LL BE THRILLED.

To Ellen From Nate

HMM!... WHAT COULD **THIS** BE?

OH, IT... IT'S NOTHING, REALLY.

I COULDN'T FIGURE OUT WHAT TO GET YOU, ELLEN. I WENT INTO A ZILLION DIFFERENT STORES, BUT NOTHING SEEMED RIGHT.

FINALLY, I DECIDED I'D JUST **MAKE** YOU A PRESENT WITH WHATEVER MATERIALS I COULD COME UP WITH.

I CLIPPED STUFF OUT OF YOUR FAVORITE MAGAZINES... FOUND PICTURES OF YOUR FAVORITE SINGERS AND MOVIE STARS... COLLECTED PHOTOS FROM YOUR FRIENDS AND CLASSMATES...

IT TOOK **DAYS**, BUT FINALLY I FINISHED IT! A COLLAGE!...

...A COLLAGE IN THE SHAPE OF YOUR SILHOUETTE.

HOW **SWEET**!

merry CHRISTMAS!!

★☆★☆★☆★☆
Celebrity
INTER-
VIEW!

with:
BIFF BIFFWELL!

Friends, I'm chatting today with the big fella himself... SANTA CLAUS!

Season's greetings, Biff!

Santa, I've often wondered.. what's the most FRUST-RATING part of your job?

These LETTERS, Biff!

Take THIS one, for example: a boy named NATE WRIGHT has asked me to bring him a DOG!

Sounds simple enough!

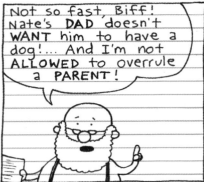

Not so fast, Biff! Nate's DAD doesn't WANT him to have a dog!... And I'm not ALLOWED to overrule a PARENT!

That DOES sound frust-rating!

And UNFAIR! Just another case of a parent being SELFISH!

So what do you do? Punish Nate's Dad?

Hey, I'm Santa Claus! It's not in my job description to punish parents!

So instead, I pick up the phone and call my friend MOTHER NATURE!

Mother Nature? What can SHE do?